Up and O...

Written by Karra McFarlane

Collins

It can go on up.

It tips up and off.

Bill gets the ill man.

The man can go up.

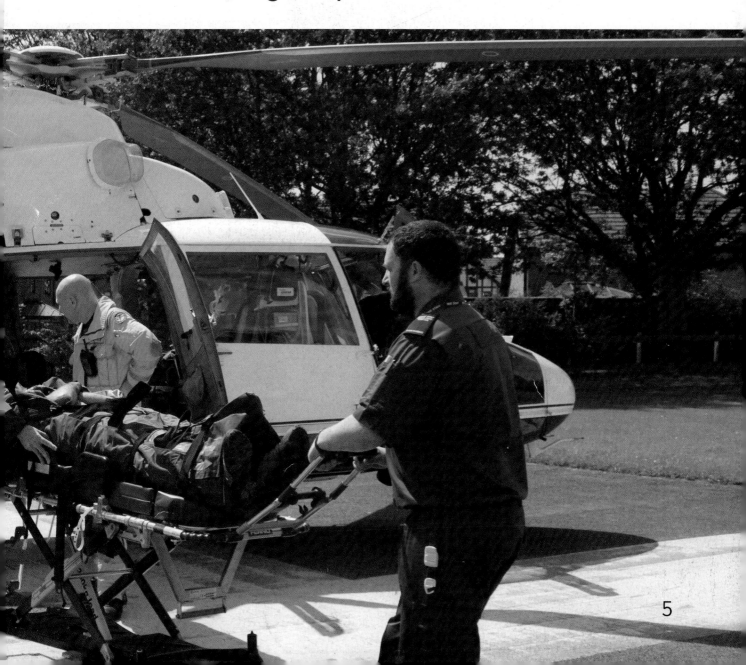

It can go on up.

It tips up and off.

Lin can not miss Fin.

Lin can pick Fin up.

It can go on up.

It tips up and off.

Len gets the big dog.

The big dog licks Len.

SS

14

15

After reading

Letters and Sounds: Phase 2

Word count: 60

Focus phonemes: /f/ /b/ /g/ /o/ /e/ /u/ /l/ /c/ ck, ll, ss, ff

Common exception words: the, go

Curriculum links: Understanding the World

Early learning goals: Reading: use phonic knowledge to decode regular words and read them aloud accurately, read some common irregular words; Understanding: answer "how" and "why" questions about their experiences and in response to stories or events

Developing fluency

- Your child may enjoy hearing you read the book.
- You could take turns to read a page, modelling reading with lots of expression.

Phonic practice

- Say the word **tips**. Ask your child if they can sound out each of the letter sounds in the word **tips** (on page 3) t/i/p/s and then blend them.
- Ask your child if they can think of any words that rhyme with tips. (e.g. *dips, sips, skips*)
- Look at the "I spy sounds" pages (14–15). Say the sounds together. How many items can your child spot that have the /f/ sound in them (e.g. *fish, factory, flippers, starfish*) or "ss" in them? (e.g. *grass, dress*)

Extending vocabulary

- Look at the word **big** used to describe the dog on pages 12 and 13. Ask your child if they can think of any other words we could use to describe the dog. (e.g. *golden, tall, friendly*)
- Now look at page 4. Ask your child if they can think of any other words we could use instead of **ill**. (e.g. *poorly, sick, injured*)